Workbook for
Electricity and Basic Electronics

by
Stephen R. Matt
Vocational Director/Assistant Principal
Winder-Barrow High School

Publisher
The Goodheart-Willcox Company, Inc.
Tinley Park, Illinois

Introduction

This workbook is designed for use with the text, **Electricity and Basic Electronics**. The chapters in the workbook correspond to those in the text and should be completed after reading the appropriate text chapter.

Each chapter of the workbook includes objectives, instructions, questions, problems, and activities. The various types of questions include identification, true or false, multiple choice, fill-in-the-blank, and essay. Problems require that you apply what you read in the text and sketching circuit designs and analyzing their features. Activities include connecting actual circuits and producing electronic products. Activities involving the use of electrical equipment and circuit design should be done only under the supervision of your instructor. Failing to do so may result in serious or fatal injuries.

Reading **Electricity and Basic Electronics** and using this workbook will provide you with a solid background in electrical fundamentals, electronic principles, and circuit design. Mastering this information will prepare you to further increase your knowledge through additional readings and practical experience.

Stephen R. Matt

Contents

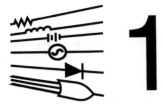

1 Learning and Applying the Fundamentals

Name _____   Score _____

Date_____ Class/period_____   Instructor _____

OVERALL OBJECTIVE: You will be able to explain what electricity is and identify the components of a simple circuit.

DIRECTIONS: Carefully read Chapter 1 of the text. Then complete the following questions and problems.

1. List four of the most important uses of electricity in your everyday living.

   _____

   _____

   _____

   _____

2. List four items which do NOT in some way depend on electricity for their existence.

   _____

   _____

   _____

   _____

3. The three necessary parts of a completed circuit include: 3. _____
   a. Source, path, and load.
   b. Lamp, battery, and switch.
   c. Battery, wire, and switch.
   d. Electrons, battery, and load.

4. The purpose of a switch is to _____

   _____

   _____

5. In the boxes below, draw symbols for each electrical component.

A. Cell	B. Battery	C. Speaker	D. Lamp

E. Wires crossing	F. Wires connected	G. Door bell

6. Use the symbols you have learned in this chapter to diagram a simple circuit. Label the components.

7. Label the parts of the helium atom shown below.

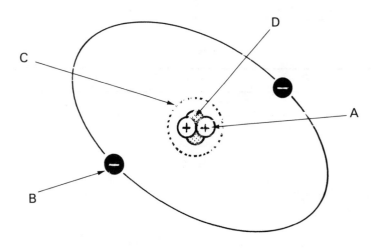

A. _____

B. _____

C. _____

D. _____

8. An atom is made up of:
   a. Neutrons, protons, and ions.
   b. Ions, electrons, and protons.
   c. Electrons, neutrons, and protons.
   d. Neutrons, electrons, and ions.

8. _____

9. The movement of electricity is from:
   a. Negative to positive.
   b. Positive to negative.
   c. Neutral to negative.
   d. Neutral to positive.

9. _____

10. In a circuit with a battery, the electrons flow:
    a. Out of the positive terminal.
    b. Out of the negative terminal.
    c. From the electrolyte.
    d. From the battery acid.

10. _____

8

2 Sources of Electricity

Name _____   Score _____

Date_____ Class/period_____   Instructor _____

OVERALL OBJECTIVE: You will be able to explain the properties of magnetism and identify methods of making, converting, generating, and storing electricity.

DIRECTIONS: Carefully read Chapter 2 of the text. Then complete the following questions, problems, and activities.

1. List the five general methods of making, converting, or generating electricity and give at least one example of each.

   _____

   _____

   _____

   _____

   _____

2. A dry cell: 2. _____
   a. Is an electrical generating device which uses only dry chemicals.
   b. Is the same thing as a dead cell.
   c. Produces alternating current.
   d. Uses an electrolyte to help produce electricity.

3. A continuity tester is used to: 3. _____
   a. Locate matching wire ends in a wiring harness.
   b. Measure resistance of the large coils found inside transformers.
   c. Test inductors.
   d. Check the voltage of a battery.

4. The electrolyte found in a storage battery usually is: 4. _____
   a. Distilled water.
   b. Tap water.
   c. Acid.
   d. Lead.

5. Label the components of the buzzer circuit schematic shown below.

A. _____

B. _____

C. _____

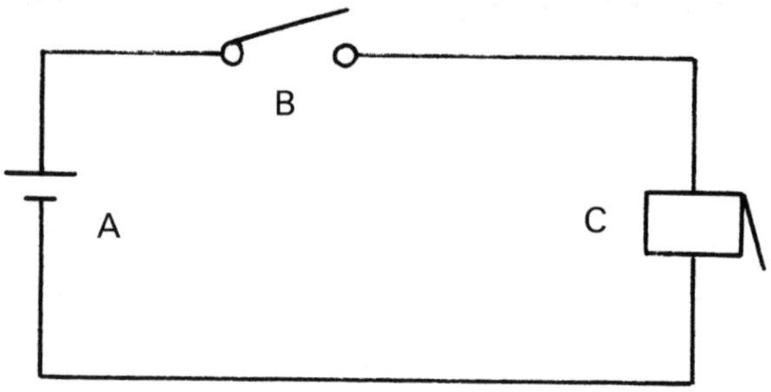

6. The device used to tell whether or not a battery is fully charged is called a:
   a. Terminal post checker.
   b. Hydrometer.
   c. Density checker.
   d. Specific gravity comparator.

6. _____

7. In colder regions of the country, a battery could freeze if the:
   a. Specific gravity of the electrolyte lowers to that of water.
   b. Specific gravity of the electrolyte gets too high.
   c. Positive and negative plates get covered with electrolyte.
   d. Vent cap has a hole in it.

7. _____

MATCHING: Match terms which are closely related. Print the appropriate letter next to the number of the similar term in the left column.

8. Photovoltaic	A. Crystal.	8. _____
9. Piezoelectric	B. Two dissimilar metals.	9. _____
10. Photoelectric	C. Highly sensitive meter.	10. _____
11. Thermocouple	D. Light sensing device.	11. _____
12. Galvanometer	E. Convert light energy to electricity.	12. _____
	F. Convert low voltage current into high voltage current.	

ACTIVITIES: The following activities are designed to help you understand the properties of magnetism. Obtain the necessary materials from your instructor.

13. Obtain a piece of wax paper approximately 12 in. by 12 in. in size. Place a bar magnet flat under the wax paper. Sprinkle iron filings on the wax paper. Tap the paper gently until the filings form a pattern between the poles of the magnet. In the space below, make a sketch which shows the pattern.

14. Remove the filings from the wax paper you used in exercise 13. Replace the bar magnet with a horseshoe magnet so its U-shape is under the sheet of wax paper. Again, sprinkle iron filings on the wax paper and tap the paper gently until the filings form a pattern. In the space below, make a sketch which shows the pattern.

15. Tie a string in the middle of a bar magnet and cover both ends with tape so that you cannot see the north or south pole marks. Hang the magnet so that it is free to turn. Spin the magnet very slowly in a circle, then allow it to come to rest. Place a mark on the taped end which points at the geographic North Pole.

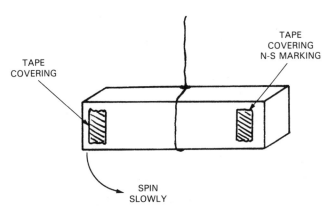

Before removing the tape, which magnet pole do you think is pointing north? ___(A)___. Remove the tape from the magnet. Which end was actually pointing toward the North geographic pole? ___(B)___

A. _____

B. _____

16. Place the north pole of a second bar magnet near the north pole of the hanging magnet.

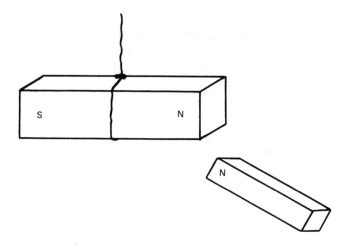

What happens to the two magnets? _____

_____

_____

17. Use information from the text and the previous exercises to answer the following question: If like poles repel, why does the north pole of a compass needle point toward the North geographic pole?_____

_____

_____

3 Conductors and Insulators

Name _____   Score _____

Date_____ Class/period_____   Instructor _____

OVERALL OBJECTIVE: You will be able to identify materials which allow electricity to flow and those which prevent it.

DIRECTIONS: Carefully read Chapter 3 of the text. Then complete the following questions and problems. Obtain materials, tools, and supplies from your instructor for the activities.

1. List five materials which would make good conductors.

_____

_____

_____

_____

_____

2. Obtain one foot samples of three types of conducting material. Using an ohmmeter, measure the resistance for each material and record your findings below. (Consult your instructor for the proper use of an ohmmeter.)

CONDUCTING MATERIAL	RESISTANCE (OHMS)

3. Obtain three different sizes of stranded wire. List the size of each. Strip the insulation off the last inch of the wire, being careful not to break any of the strands. Count the number of strands in each of the wires. Record your findings below.

SIZE (DIAMETER)	NUMBER OF STRANDS

4. List five materials which would make good insulators.

_____

_____

_____

_____

_____

5. Obtain equal length samples of three types of insulating material. Using an ohmmeter, measure the resistance for each material and record your findings below.

INSULATING MATERIAL	RESISTANCE (OHMS)

6. True or false? A conductor has higher resistance to electron flow than does an insulator.

6. _____

7. Rank the four materials listed below based on their ability to conduct current, best to worst.
Nichrome
Aluminum
Silver
Carbon

A. _____
B. _____
C. _____
D. _____

8. A cable is:
   a. A steel wire used for connecting a television set.
   b. An insulating material.
   c. A braided connector.
   d. An assembly of two or more wires inside a common covering.

8. _____

9. Which wire type is best suited for use as a lamp cord?
   a. Stranded.
   b. Solid.
   c. Shielded remote control cable.
   d. Coaxial cable.

9. _____

10. Which of the following is the largest diameter wire?
    a. 22 NSF.
    b. 12 AWG.
    c. 06 BFG.
    d. 00 THL.

10. _____

11. Which of the following is NOT correct?
    a. Undersize wire can cause overheating problems.
    b. A flow of one amp results when many billions of electrons flow past a point in one second.
    c. Resistance wire is found in heating elements.
    d. Fuses are measured using the circular mil as a reference.

11. _____

12. Which of the following is NOT a type of fuse?
    a. High resistance.
    b. Slow blowing.
    c. Cartridge.
    d. Dual element.

12. _____

13. Which of the following is the most common type of switch found in your home?
    a. Double-pole, double-throw.
    b. Double-pole, single-throw.
    c. Single-pole, single-throw.
    d. Single-pole, double-throw.

13. _____

14. Most solder used in electrical work is a mixture of ____(A)____ percent ____(B)____ and ____(C)____ percent ____(D)____.

A. _____
B. _____
C. _____
D. _____

15. Which of the following statements describes a good solder joint?
    a. Dull in appearance and smooth.
    b. Dull in appearance, with beads of solder.
    c. Shiny in appearance and smooth.
    d. Shiny in appearance with lumps.

15. _____

16. The _____ contains the general rules and regulations that contractors, builders, and manufacturers must follow for proper installation and routing of wires.
    a. National Electrical Code.
    b. National Electrical Manufacturers Association.
    c. American Society for Electrical Devices.
    d. Association of Electrical Engineers.

16. _____

4 Resistors and Capacitors

Name _____   Score _____

Date_____ Class/period_____   Instructor _____

OVERALL OBJECTIVE: You will be able to identify the function of resistors and capacitors, and determine resistance values.

DIRECTIONS: Carefully read Chapter 4 of the text. Then complete the following questions, problems, and activities.

1. Select five different resistors with varying color bands. Record the color of the bands and calculate the resistor's value and tolerance. Place your answers in the chart below.

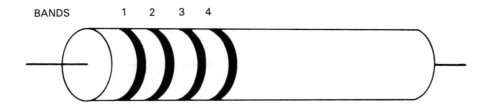

BANDS   1   2   3   4

RESISTOR NUMBER	BAND COLORS				VALUE	TOLERANCE
	First	Second	Third	Fourth		
1						
2						
3						
4						
5						

2. Using the value and tolerance values of the five resistors, calculate the minimum and maximum values and record your answers below. Show your work on the side.

RESISTOR NUMBER	VALUE	
	Minimum	Maximum
1		
2		
3		
4		
5		

3. Now that you have calculated the labeled resistance value, measure the actual resistance of each resistor using an ohmmeter. Record your answer below and also state whether the measured value falls into the range of the labeled value calculated in exercise 2.

RESISTOR NUMBER	MEASURED VALUE	FALLS INTO LABELED RANGE (YES OR NO)
1		
2		
3		
4		
5		

4. List three reasons why there might be a difference between the color coded values and actual meter readings of the resistor.

_____

_____

_____

5. List four types of fixed resistors.

_____

_____

_____

_____

6. Convert the resistor values on the left to the new measurement values on the right.

A. 2700 ohms   _____ kilohms   A. _____

B. 8.5 megohms   _____ ohms   B. _____

C. 25 kilohms   _____ ohms   C. _____

D. 48 megohms   _____ kilohms   D. _____

E. 65,000,000 ohms   _____ kilohms   E. _____

7. Obtain four potentiometers and label the leads A, B, and C.

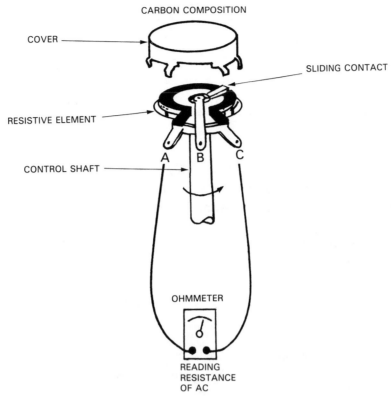

Turn the adjustment knob fully clockwise and measure the resistance values between all three leads. Repeat the process in the fully counterclockwise direction, and once again with the adjustment knob about in the middle. Record your measurements in the chart below.

KNOB DIRECTION	LEADS TESTED	POTENTIOMETERS			
		1	2	3	4
CLOCKWISE	AB				
	BC				
	AC				
COUNTER-CLOCKWISE	AB				
	BC				
	AC				
MIDDLE	AB				
	BC				
	AC				

8. Based on the readings you took in Exercise 7, what three observations can you make?

   A. _____

   _____

   B. _____

   _____

   C. _____

   _____

9. The fifth band on a resistor is used to describe:
   a. The expected failure rate per thousand hours of use.
   b. The expected failure rate per thousand resistors manufactured.
   c. How much current it will carry.
   d. The expected shelf life of the resistor.

   9. _____

10. When installing a resistor in a circuit, the end with the colored bands:
   a. Must be connected to the negative lead.
   b. Must be connected to the positive lead.
   c. Can be connected to either lead of the circuit.
   d. Must be elevated for better heat retention.

   10. _____

11. A thermistor:
   a. Is a resistor used with very high voltages.
   b. Increases resistance the same as a potentiometer does.
   c. Is the same as a trimmer resistor.
   d. Changes resistance with changes in temperature.

   11. _____

12. A capacitor:
   a. Increases the current.
   b. Is used to store a charge in a circuit.
   c. Lowers the resistance of a circuit.
   d. Is used instead of a battery for low voltage circuits.

   12. _____

13. The three factors which affect capacitance are:
   a. Surface area, distance between plates, and insulating material.
   b. Size, length, and voltage of the circuit.
   c. Diameter, voltage, and current in the circuit.
   d. Material, dielectric, and working voltage.

   13. _____

14. What definition below best describes a dielectric?   14. _____
    a. The binder material used to make a resistor.
    b. The material used when constructing the insulating
       cover on a cable.
    c. The paste substance used to make a battery.
    d. The insulating material used to make a capacitor.

15. Before you pick up any capacitor, you should: 15. _____
    a. Check its working voltage.
    b. Discharge it.
    c. Touch the two leads together.
    d. Inspect it for burns.

16. Convert the capacitor values on the left to the equivalent values using the measurement on
    the right.
    A. 0.003 farads   _____ microfarads   A. _____
    B. 100 microfarads   _____ farads   B. _____
    C. .00005 microfarads   _____ picofarads   C. _____
    D. 125,000 picofarads   _____ microfarads   D. _____

17. Which type of capacitor should be reformed slowly after   17. _____
    a period of not being used to prevent damage from a sud-
    den surge?
    a. Electrolytic.
    b. Ceramic.
    c. Mica.
    d. Film.

18. If exact replacement capacitors are not available, you   18. _____
    should substitute:
    a. Those with a lower working voltage.
    b. A capacitor having higher capacitance.
    c. One having a larger diameter.
    d. A capacitor with the same rating, but higher working
       voltage.

19. Which of the following is NOT a precaution that should   19. _____
    be followed when installing replacement capacitors?
    a. Be sure that the new leads are the same length as the
       old ones.
    b. Solder electrolytic capacitors in position with the plus
       lead toward the negative pole of the power supply.
    c. Use a heat sink between the capacitor and the solder
       joint to prevent damage to the dielectric.
    d. Make sure the new capacitor is soldered in place the
       same way as the old one to prevent a possible shift
       in capacitance.

5 Ohm's Law

Name _____   Score _____

Date_____ Class/period_____   Instructor _____

OVERALL OBJECTIVE: You will be able to apply Ohm's Law to find the current, voltage, and resistance of a circuit.

DIRECTIONS: Carefully read Chapter 5 of the text. Then complete the following questions, problems, and activities.

1. Take readings of your home electric meter and record the information on the chart below.

DAY	METER READING	KILOWATT USED SINCE LAST READING
1		0
2		
3		
4		

2. Find the cost of electricity being charged by your local power company. Then calculate the daily cost of electricity used between days 1 and 2, days 2 and 3, and days 3 and 4. Record this information in the chart below.

PERIOD	COST (Cost = _____ per kilowatt hour)
Days 1 to 2	
Days 2 to 3	
Days 3 to 4	

3. Check the rating/information plate on the following electrical appliances. Record the amps and watts. Then determine the cost for operating that appliance for one hour. Use the kWh (kilowatt hour) cost you used in Exercise 2.

APPLIANCE	AMPS	WATTS	OPERATING COST PER HOUR
Can opener			
Clothes dryer			
Electric range			
Lamp			
Refrigerator			
Stereo			
Television			
Toaster			
Hair Dryer			

4. Find the circuit breaker/fuse box in your home. Add the amperage of each breaker or fuse to determine the maximum amount of current your house wiring can safely carry. Use the chart below to count the number of breakers in each amperage range.

BREAKER RATING	NUMBER OF BREAKERS	TOTAL AMPS
15 amps		
20 amps		
30 amps		
50 amps		
Other _____ amps		

TOTAL HOUSE AMPERAGE _____

MATCHING: Match terms which are closely related. Print the appropriate letter next to the number at right.

5. Current	A. Watt	5. _____
6. Resistance	B. Ampere	6. _____
7. Volt	C. Ohm	7. _____
8. Power	D. Electromotive force	8. _____
	E. Farads	

Ohm's Law

Match formulas to the related term. Print the appropriate formula's letter next to the number at right.

9. Ohm   A. $E = I \times R$ 9. _____

10. Volt   B. $R = E/I$ 10. _____

11. Amp   C. $P = I \times F$ 11. _____

12. Watt   D. $I = E/R$ 12. _____

                E. $P = I \times R$

13. Convert the amperage values on the left to the new measure of amperage on the right.

    A. 0.01 amps   _____ milliamps   A. _____

    B. 635 mA   _____ amps   B. _____

    C. 3/10 amps   _____ mA   C. _____

    D. 0.000285 amps   _____ microamps   D. _____

14. How much power would be used by a 150 watt light bulb?   14. _____
    a. 110 volts.
    b. 1.3 amps.
    c. 1.4 ohms.
    d. 150 watts.

15. According to Ohm's Law, you can determine the: 15. _____
    a. Voltage by knowing the current.
    b. Current by knowing the resistance.
    c. Resistance by knowing the voltage.
    d. Resistance if you know the current and voltage.

16. Which of the following current values is the largest?   16. _____
    a. 350 mA.
    b. 0.005 A.
    c. 485,000 microamps.
    d. 295 watts.

17. The chart below gives the amps, voltage, and resistance for five circuits. However, some of the data are missing. Use Ohm's Law to solve for the missing value.

CIRCUIT	VOLTAGE	AMPERAGE	RESISTANCE
A.	6		7.9
B.	12	2.1	
C.		.07	2.2
D.	.3		10.3
E.	5.4	8.1	

 **6** Series Circuits

Name _____   Score _____

Date_____ Class/period_____   Instructor _____

OVERALL OBJECTIVE: You will be able to identify the characteristics of a series circuit and apply Ohm's Law to calculate total resistance and voltage drop.

DIRECTIONS: Carefully read Chapter 6 of the text. Then complete the following questions, problems, and activities.

1. Obtain three 1.5 volt lamps. Check them to be sure that none are burned out. Connect the three lamps in series to a variable power supply and attach a voltmeter as shown in the diagram below.

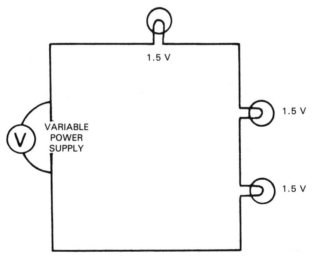

Slowly increase the voltage until all three lamps are burning brightly. Record the voltage readings for the following three conditions.

A. Voltage when lamps are not lit.   A. _____

B. Voltage when lamps just begin to light.   B. _____

C. Voltage when lamps are at full brilliance. C. _____

2. Obtain two 1.5 volt lamps and one 3 volt lamp. Check to be sure none of them are burned out. Connect the lamps in series to a variable power supply and voltmeter as shown in the diagram below.

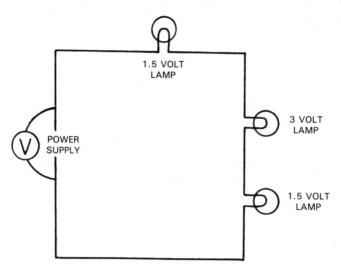

Slowly increase the voltage and note the results. Then, answer the questions below.

A. Which bulb(s) reached full brightness first?   A. _____

B. What is the voltage when full brightness is reached   B. _____
   by at least one bulb?

C. How much voltage can be applied without the danger   C. _____
   of burning out a bulb?

D. What conclusion do you reach based on the results of your observations?

_____

_____

_____

_____

3. Using the circuit in Exercise 1, first turn off the power, then remove the bulb nearest the power supply. Turn the power back on. What happens?

_____

_____

_____

4. Replace the bulb you removed in Exercise 3 and remove the middle bulb. Turn on the power supply. What happens?

_____

_____

5. What conclusions can you make based on the results of Exercises 3 and 4?

_____

_____

6. Using the correct schematic symbols, diagram a series circuit which consists of a 6 volt battery and three 400 ohm resistors. Calculate the current in the circuit, showing the correct formula and your work.

The current in the circuit is _____.

6. _____

7. If four 1.5 volt flashlight batteries are placed in the flashlight:
   a. Correctly, there will be 6 volts available.
   b. Correctly, there will be 3 volts available.
   c. Incorrectly, 6 volts will be available.
   d. Incorrectly, 12 volts will be available.

7. _____

8. A continuity light can be used to:
   a. Check the voltage of a power supply.
   b. Measure the current in a circuit.
   c. Check for a blown fuse.
   d. Check the resistance of a circuit.

8. _____

9. The schematic below shows a series circuit with three resistors and a single power supply. An ammeter is placed in the circuit to measure current. Voltmeters are placed across each of the resistors. The chart below the diagram gives values for the power supply and resistors in seven different circuits. Calculate the current for each circuit to three decimal places, then calculate the voltage drop across each resistor to two decimal places.

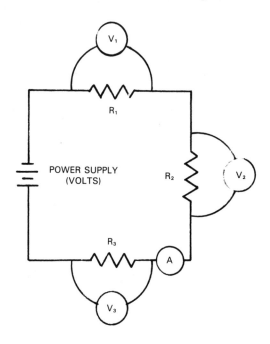

CIRCUIT	POWER SUPPLY (VOLTS)	RESISTANCE (OHMS)			CURRENT	VOLTAGE DROP		
		R_1	R_2	R_3	A	V_1	V_2	V_3
A.	90	10	22	15				
B.	110	30	15	45				
C.	120	20	33	16				
D.	240	15	25	42				
E.	30	40	47	24				
F.	6	10	10	10				
G.	12	15	15	15				

10. Obtain three 10 ohm resistors and a 6 volt dc power supply. Also get an ammeter and a voltmeter. Connect the circuit as shown in circuit F of Exercise 9. Record the current and voltage drops across each of the three resistors.

Is there any difference between your measured amounts and those you calculated in Exercise 9?

_____

If so, how can you explain the difference? _____

_____

_____

_____

7 Parallel Circuits

Name _____   Score _____

Date_____ Class/period_____   Instructor _____

OVERALL OBJECTIVE: You will be able to identify the characteristics of a parallel circuit and apply Ohm's Law to calculate resistance, current, and voltage in various parts of a circuit.

DIRECTIONS: Carefully read Chapter 7 of the text. Then complete the following questions, problems, and activities.

1. Obtain three 1.5 volt lamps. Check them to be sure that none are burned out. Connect the three lamps in parallel with a variable power supply and attach a volt meter as shown in the diagram below.

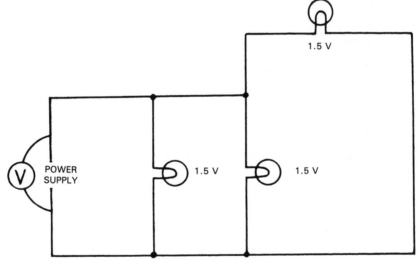

Slowly increase the voltage until all three lamps are burning brightly. Record your voltage readings for the following three conditions.

A. Voltage when lamps are not lit.   A. _____

B. Voltage when lamps just begin to light.   B. _____

C. Voltage when lamps are at full brilliance.   C. _____

2. Obtain two 1.5 volt lamps and one 3 volt lamp. Check to be sure none of them are burned out. Connect the lamps in parallel with a variable power supply and attach a voltmeter as shown in the diagram below.

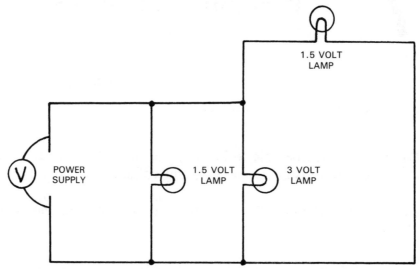

Slowly increase the voltage and note the results. Then answer the following questions.

A. Which bulb(s) reached full brightness first?   A. _____

B. What is the voltage when full brightness is reached   B. _____
   by at least one bulb?

C. How much voltage should be applied without the   C. _____
   danger of burning out a bulb?

D. What conclusion can you make about the voltage in a parallel circuit based on the results of your observations?

_____

_____

_____

_____

3. Using the circuit in Exercise 1, first turn off the power, then remove the 1.5 volt bulb nearest the power supply. Turn the power back on. What happens?

_____

_____

4. Replace the bulb you removed in Exercise 3 and remove the middle bulb. Turn the power supply back on. What happens?

_____

_____

5. What conclusions can you make based on the results of Exercises 3 and 4?

_____

_____

6. Using the correct schematic symbols, diagram a parallel circuit with three 900 ohm resistors connected in parallel with a 6 volt battery. Calculate the current in the circuit, showing the correct formula and your work.

The current in the circuit is _____.

6. _____

7. If four 1.5 volt dry cells are connected in parallel:
   a. 6 volts will be available.
   b. 4.5 volts will be available.
   c. 3 volts will be available.
   d. 1.5 volts will be available.

7. _____

8. What is the advantage of connecting cells in parallel?
   a. The voltage will be increased.
   b. The resistance will be increased.
   c. The load current can be shared between cells.
   d. Lamps connected to the circuit will burn brighter than
      if connected in a series circuit.

8. _____

33

9. The schematic below shows a parallel circuit with three resistors and a single power supply. Five ammeters are placed at strategic locations in the circuit. The chart below the diagram gives values to the power supply and resistors for four different circuits. You must calculate total resistance for the circuits, then calculate the current flow at each ammeter.

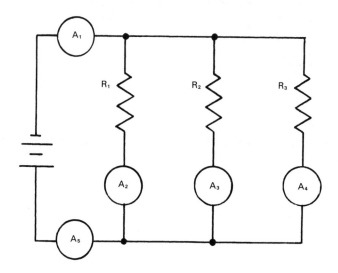

CIRCUIT	POWER SUPPLY (VOLTS)	RESISTANCE (OHMS)			TOTAL RESIST-ANCE	CURRENT (AMPERES)				
		R_1	R_2	R_3		A_1	A_2	A_3	A_4	A_5
A.	100	500	500	1000						
B.	12	10	10	20						
C.	120	20	40	60						
D.	90	30	30	30						

10. Obtain three 30 ohm resistors, a 90 volt power supply, and five ammeters. Connect the circuit as shown in the diagram of Exercise 9. Record the current at each of the five ammeters. Compare your measurements with the values you calculated in Circuit D of Exercise 9. Is there any difference? If so, how can you explain the difference?

_____

_____

_____

_____

_____

8 Series Parallel Circuits

Name _____   Score _____

Date_____ Class/period_____   Instructor _____

OVERALL OBJECTIVE: You will be able to identify a series parallel circuit, and apply Ohm's Law to calculate total resistance, voltage, and current in any part of the circuit.

DIRECTIONS: Carefully read Chapter 8 of the text. Then complete the following questions, problems, and activities.

1. Obtain three 3 volt lamps. Check them to be sure that none are burned out. Connect them in series parallel to a variable power supply as shown in the schematic below. Attach a volt meter as shown.

Be prepared to record your voltage readings for the following three conditions. Then slowly increase the voltage until all three lamps are burning brightly.

A. Voltage when lamps are not lit.   A. _____

B. Voltage when at least one lamp begins to light.   B. _____

C. Voltage when at least one lamp is at full brightness.   C. _____

D. When at least one lamp is at full brightness, are there any other lamps which are also at full brightness?

_____

_____

2. Obtain two 3 volt lamps and one 1.5 volt lamp. Check them to be sure none are burned out. Connect the lamps in series parallel to a variable power source as shown in the diagram below. Place a voltmeter across the power supply.

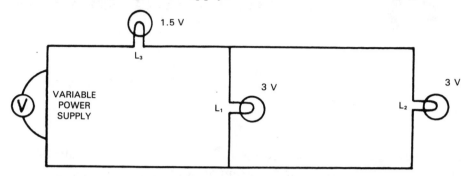

Slowly increase the voltage and record your findings to the following questions.

A. Which of the lamps reached full brightness first?   A. _____

B. What is the voltage when at least one lamp is at full brightness?   B. _____

C. What is the maximum voltage that could be applied without burning out any of the bulbs?   C. _____

D. What conclusion can you make about how voltage is divided in a series parallel circuit?

_____

_____

_____

3. Connect three 3 volt lamps and a variable power supply as you did for Exercise 1. Before turning the power supply on, remove lamp L_1 (refer to the diagram in Exercise 1). Attach a voltmeter across the power supply. Turn on the power supply. What happens to the remaining two lamps?

_____

_____

_____

4. Replace lamp L_1 in the circuit you connected for Exercise 3. (Make sure the power supply is OFF). Now remove lamp L_3 from the circuit (refer to the diagram in Exercise 1). Turn on the power supply and increase the voltage. Record what happens.

_____

_____

_____

5. Using the correct schematic symbols, diagram a series parallel circuit which consists of a 24 volt dc power supply, a 2400 ohm and 3600 ohm resistor in parallel, and a third unknown resistance connected in series.

6. For the circuit diagrammed in Exercise 5, calculate the value for the unknown resistor if the circuit current is 10 mA.

6. _____

7. For the circuit diagrammed in Exercise 5, calculate the current value if the third resistor is rated at 8160 ohms.

7. _____

8. If three 1.5 volt dry cells are connected in series parallel:
   a. 6 volts will be available.
   b. 4.5 volts will be available.
   c. 3 volts will be available.
   d. 1.5 volts will be available.

8. _____

9. What is the advantage of connecting capacitors in parallel?
   a. Working voltage will be increased.
   b. Capacitance will be increased.
   c. Load current can be shared between capacitors.
   d. Capacitance will be decreased.

9. _____

10. When capacitors are placed in parallel, capacitance will:
    a. Increase because the plate area is larger.
    b. Increase because the distance between the plates is increased.
    c. Decrease because the plate area is larger.
    d. Decrease because the distance between the plates is decreased.

10. _____

11. The schematic below shows a series parallel circuit with three resistors and a single power supply. Three ammeters are placed at strategic locations in the circuit. The chart below the diagram gives values to the power supply, resistors, and ammeters. However, in each circuit, one value is missing. Using Ohm's Law, calculate the missing value.

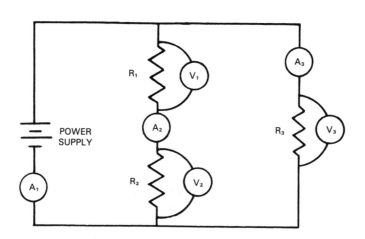

CIRCUIT	POWER SUPPLY (VOLTS)	RESISTANCE (OHMS)			CURRENT		
		R_1	R_2	R_3	A_1	A_2	A_3
A.	24		12	24	2	1	1
B.	12	10	10	30		0.6	0.4
C.	90	15		90	2.5	1.5	1
D.	110	30	30	15	9.16	1.833	
E.	240	60	60		6	2	4

12. Obtain three resistors of different values and a 12 volt power supply. Also obtain an ohm-meter, voltmeter, and ammeter, or simply use a multimeter. Proceed through the following steps and record your results in the chart on next page.
   A. Calculate the manufactured resistance of each of your resistors. This can be done by reading the color bands. Mark the resistors R_1, R_2, and R_3. Record their resistance in the "Calculated Resistance" portion of the chart.
   B. Measure the resistance of each resistor. Remember to zero your ohmmeter first. Record the measured resistance on the chart.
   C. Connect the resistors in series parallel to the power supply as shown in the diagram for Exercise 11. Do not turn on the power supply yet.
   D. Calculate the current readings for the three ammeters placed in the circuit. Record your results.

E. Calculate the voltage drop across each of the resistors. Record your results.
F. Turn on the power supply. Make current readings using an ammeter. Remember, the ammeter must be placed in series with the circuit. Record your measurements on the chart.
G. Take voltage drop readings across the resistors. Record your readings on the chart.

	RESISTANCE (OHMS)			CURRENT (AMPS)			VOLTAGE DROP (VOLTS)		
	R_1	R_2	R_3	A_1	A_2	A_3	V_1	V_2	V_3
CALCULATED									
MEASURED									

13. Referring to Exercise 11, is there any difference between the values you calculated and those you measured? If so, how do you explain the difference?

_____
_____
_____
_____
_____

14. Three switches are connected in series with a load. All three switches are closed to complete the circuit. Suppose the power supply is 6 volts. How much voltage is supplied to the load?
   a. 2 volts.
   b. 3 volts.
   c. None, because the voltage drop across each of the three switches is 2 volts.
   d. 6 volts.

14. _____

15. Diagram a series parallel circuit which has the following:
    A. Power supply.
    B. Two loads in parallel to the power supply.
    C. Two loads in series with the power supply.
    D. A SPST switch.
    E. A fuse.
    F. An ammeter to monitor current.
    G. Two grounds to complete the path for the circuit.

 # 9 Meters

Name _____   Score _____

Date_____ Class/period_____   Instructor _____

OVERALL OBJECTIVE: You will be able to properly use meters to measure voltage, current, and resistance of typical circuits.

DIRECTIONS: Carefully read Chapter 9 of the text. Then complete the following questions, problems, and activities.

1. When measuring an unknown voltage or current, you should:
   a. Start with the range selector switch at its highest value.
   b. Start with the range selector switch at the lowest value.
   c. Start with the selector switch set in the "ohms" position.
   d. Start with the selector switch set in either the microvolts or microamps position.

1. _____

2. Pegging a meter results when:
   a. The voltage of the source is too low.
   b. The batteries in the meter are about dead.
   c. The pointer slams into one end of the meter scale because the range selector switch is set too low.
   d. The meter fails to read because the range selector switch is set too high.

2. _____

3. A D'Arsonval movement:
   a. Is used for meters which require coarse measurements of high current values.
   b. Is a highly accurate jeweled movement.
   c. Is the same as a digital readout meter.
   d. Requires large shunt resistors in series with the meter movement.

3. _____

4. An ammeter is always connected in _____ with the power source and load.

4. _____

5. Suppose you wish to measure the current in the dc circuit below. Connect the lead wires to their proper location on the meter. Also draw arrows on the function switch and range selector knobs to show their correct settings.

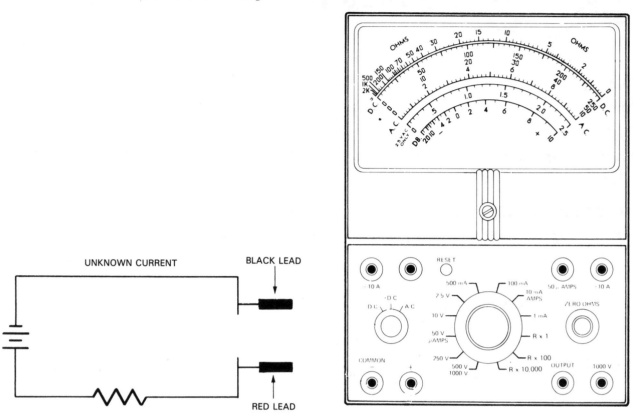

UNKNOWN CURRENT   BLACK LEAD

RED LEAD

Look at the meter diagram below to answer the following questions.

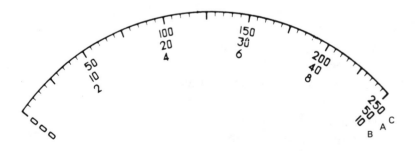

6. Which scale do you use to take readings between 1 mA and 10 mA?   6. _____

7. Which scale do you use to take readings between 0.1 mA and 1 mA?   7. _____

8. Which scale do you use to take readings between 100 mA and 500 mA?   8. _____

9. Which scale do you use to take readings between 10 mA and 100 mA?   9. _____

10. Read the current shown on each of the meters below. Record your reading next to the appropriate letter at right. Remember to look at the range selector to see what unit of measurement you are using.

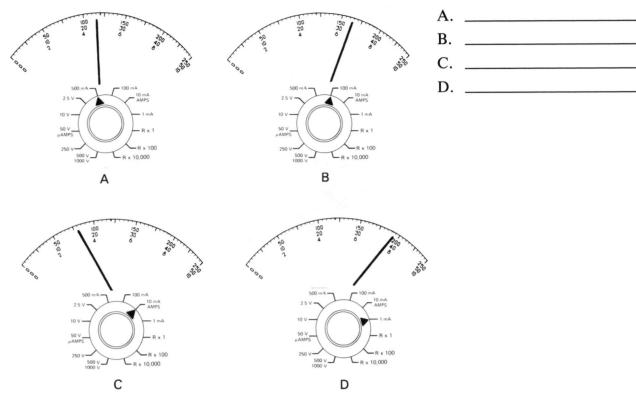

A. _____
B. _____
C. _____
D. _____

A   B

C   D

11. A damping spring is used to:
    a. Move the meter's point when a reading is taken.
    b. Convert a point type meter into a digital meter.
    c. Prevent the pointer needle from dropping too quickly after taking a reading.
    d. Prevent the meter needle from pegging.

11. _____

12. Below is a list of areas in which you can find analog meters. Give an example of how each of these areas uses a meter.
    a. Automobile dealership _____
    b. Hospital _____
    c. Power company _____
    d. Telephone company _____
    e. Electric train _____
    f. School _____

13. On the diagram below, connect the leads to test a dc circuit which could range from one to nine amps. Also put an arrow on the function switch and range selector to indicate its proper setting.

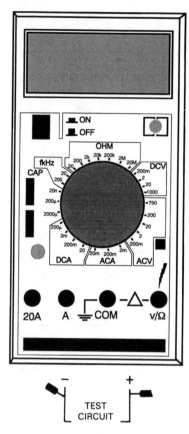

14. When using pointer-type meters, the best section of the scale to read for the greatest accuracy is:
    a. Near the center of the scale.
    b. Near the right end of the scale.
    c. Near the left end of the scale.
    d. The end where the numbers are closest together.

14. _____

15. Most multimeters are used to measure:
    a. Volts only.
    b. Amperes only.
    c. Current, voltage, and resistance.
    d. Power usage.

15. _____

16. The red lead of the meter is:
    a. Usually positive.
    b. Usually negative.
    c. Always connected to the common terminal.
    d. Always connected to the +10 A terminal.

16. _____

17. To ensure proper ohmmeter readings when testing resistance, you should:
    a. Leave the selector switch in the off position.
    b. Make readings of a 10 amp circuit.
    c. Make readings of a 10 volt circuit.
    d. Zero the meter before using any of its ranges.

17. _____

18. Whenever you work with an ohmmeter, the power must be _____ in the circuit under test.
    a. On.
    b. Off.
    c. Connected to a five volt power source.
    d. Connected to a 120 volt ac circuit.

18. _____

19. Many of the electrical meters used today are digital meters. List some inexpensive and expensive uses of digital meters you can find in your community. Think of possible uses involving speed, time, temperature and other functions.

_____

_____

_____

_____

_____

_____

_____

20. Read the voltage shown on each of the meters below. Record your reading next to the appropriate letter at right. Remember to look at the range selector to see which unit of measurement is being used.

A. _____

B. _____

C. _____

D. _____

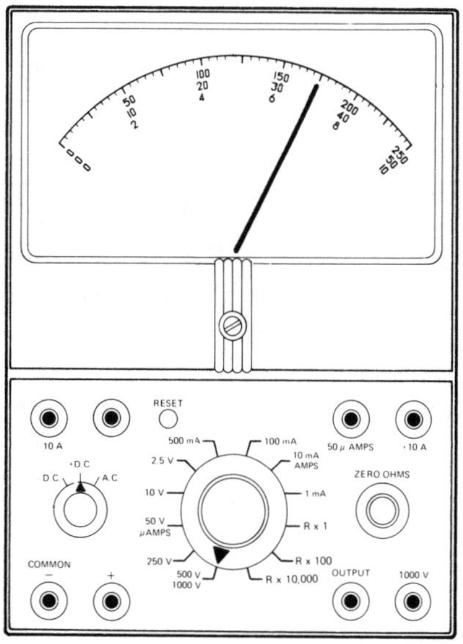

A

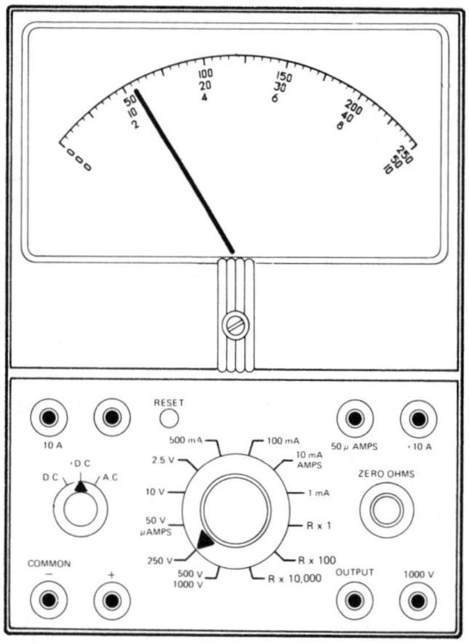

B

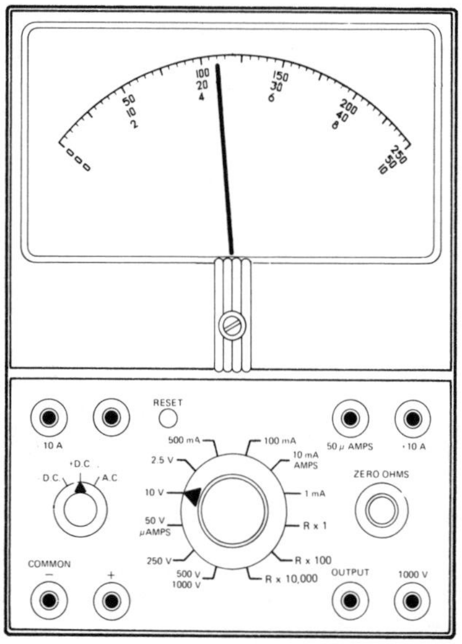

C

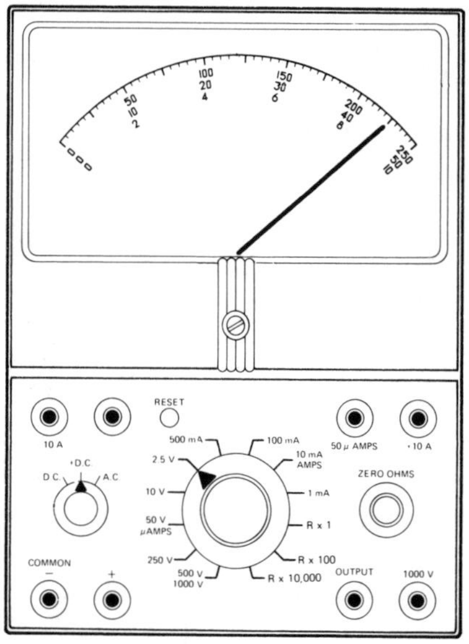

D

21. Why should you avoid touching the ends of the meter probes, even when measuring low voltage dc circuits? _____

_____

_____

_____

Name _____   Score _____

Date_____ Class/period_____   Instructor _____

OVERALL OBJECTIVE: You will be able to explain how ac voltage is produced and diagram the sine wave of an ac power source.

DIRECTIONS: Carefully read Chapter 10 of the text. Then complete the following questions, problems, and activities.

1. What is the basic difference between alternating current (ac) and direct current (dc)?
   a. Alternating current is used for lower voltage applications than is direct current.
   b. Direct current must be rectified before it can be used for a load.
   c. Alternating current reverses flow at regular intervals while direct current flows in only one direction.
   d. The polarity of direct current voltage changes at regular intervals.

1. _____

2. Alternating current can be produced by:
   a. Rotating a single wire within a magnetic field.
   b. Pulling a single wire through a magnetic field.
   c. Pulling a coil of wire through a magnetic field.
   d. Rotating a coil of wire within a magnetic field.

2. _____

3. Diagram the position of the two wire coils at points 2, 3, 4, and 5 to produce the sine wave below.

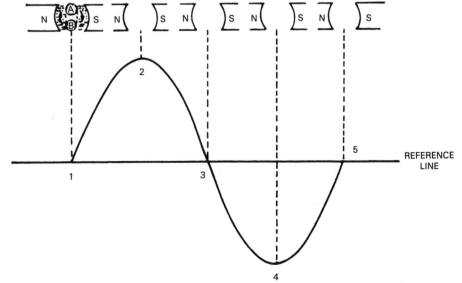

4. Label the parts of the alternating current sine wave shown below.

A. _____

B. _____

C. _____

D. _____

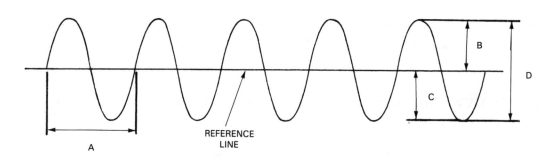

REFERENCE LINE

A

B

C

D

5. Draw a horizontal and vertical line which cross. Beginning at their intersection, draw a sine wave for an alternating current having a 4 Hz frequency and 12 volts peak to peak.

6. What is the period for an alternator which is operating at 80 cycles per second? Show the formula and your work.

6. _____

7. Which of the following will produce the most heat in a resistor?
   a. 100 volts peak-to-peak ac.
   b. 100 volts peak ac.
   c. −100 volts dc.
   d. 100 volt, 60 Hz square wave.

7. _____

8. What is the RMS value for ac having a peak value of 55   8. _____
   volts? Show the formula and your work.

9. Draw the symbol for an ac power supply.

10. In the space below, draw three cycles of a 2 Hz, 40 volt square wave. Label the amplitude, period, and mark the number of cycles completed in one second.

11. To hear the characteristics of alternating current, hook up a 30 watt speaker to a signal generator. First change the voltage using a constant 100 Hz frequency. In the chart below, record whether the tone is soft, medium, or loud.

VOLTAGE	TONE
5	
10	
20	

Set the voltage at 15 and change the frequency as instructed below. In the chart, record whether the pitch is low, medium, or high.

FREQUENCY	PITCH
100	
1000	
10,000	

12. Are the following two sine curves for current and voltage in-phase or out-of-phase?

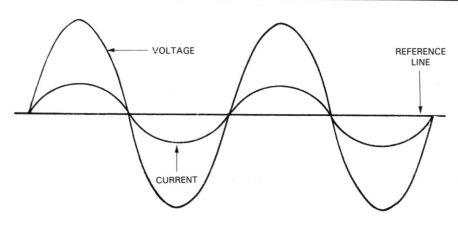

Explain why you believe your answer is correct. _____

_____

_____

_____

13. Why do signal generators produce frequencies higher than 20,000 Hz?
    a. To replicate high fidelity music.
    b. Because humans can only hear sounds above 20,000 Hz.
    c. To transmit radio and television signals.
    d. So that ac current can be carried long distances.

13. _____

14. When diagramming an ac sine wave, the reference line marks:
    a. Peak voltage.
    b. Zero voltage.
    c. Peak negative voltage.
    d. Peak-to-peak voltage.

14. _____

11 Electromagnetic Induction

Name _____   Score _____

Date _____ Class/period_____   Instructor _____

OVERALL OBJECTIVE: You will be able to induce an electrical current in a coil by electromagnetic induction and explain the purpose and function of transformers.

DIRECTIONS: Carefully read Chapter 11 of the text. Then complete the following questions, problems, and activities.

1. Obtain a bar magnet and some insulated copper bell wire. Wrap the wire in the shape of a coil about 3 in. in diameter. Connect the wire ends to a galvanometer as shown in the diagram below.

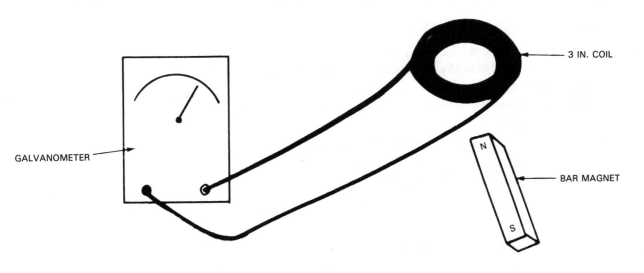

Pass the north end of the magnet slowly through the center of the coil. Then pass the south end of the magnet slowly through the center in the same direction. Record the amount of needle movement for both directions in the chart below. Next pass the magnet quickly through the coil. Do so with both the north and south ends going first. Record your results in the chart below.

END	SPEED	NEEDLE MOVEMENT (SLIGHT, HALF-SCALE, FULL-SCALE)
N	Slow	
	Fast	
S	Slow	
	Fast	

2. Repeat Exercise 1, but use a new coil about 1 1/2 in. in diameter. Use the same length of wire as you did for the 3 in. coil, but with more windings. Pass both ends of the magnet slowly and quickly through the coil. Watch the galvanometer and record your results below.

END	SPEED	NEEDLE MOVEMENT (SLIGHT, HALF-SCALE, FULL-SCALE)
N	Slow	
	Fast	
S	Slow	
	Fast	

3. Answer the following five questions based on the results you obtained in Exercises 1 and 2.
   A. Is there any difference in needle movement when you move the magnet through slow as opposed to fast?

   A. _____

   B. Does the end of the magnet which passes through first have any effect on the amount of needle movement?

   B. _____

   C. Is there greater movement of the meter needle when you use the 1 1/2 in. coil rather than the 3 in. coil?

   C. _____

   D. Which of the following would produce the most induced EMF in the wire:

   D. _____

   a. Move the magnet slowly through a small number of wire turns.
   b. Move the magnet slowly through a large number of wire turns.
   c. Move the magnet quickly through a large number of wire turns.
   d. Stop the magnet inside the coil.
   E. What happens to the meter needle if the motion of the magnet is stopped while it is still inside the coil?

   _____

   _____

4. Repeat Exercises 1 and 2, but use another type of conductor for the coil, possibly steel or aluminum. Record your results in the chart below and on the next page.

3 IN. COIL		
END	SPEED	NEEDLE MOVEMENT (SLIGHT, HALF-SCALE, FULL-SCALE)
N	Slow	
	Fast	
S	Slow	
	Fast	

Electromagnetic Induction

1 1/2 IN. COIL		
END	SPEED	NEEDLE MOVEMENT (SLIGHT, HALF-SCALE, FULL-SCALE)
N	Slow	
N	Fast	
S	Slow	
S	Fast	

Does the type of wire used for making the coil result in meter readings different than those of copper wire? _____. Explain your answer. _____

_____

_____

_____

_____

5. Electromagnetic induction is:
   a. Storing electrons for use at a later time.
   b. Creating a magnetic charge by passing electricity through a conductor.
   c. Creating resistance by passing a current through a conductor.
   d. Generating voltage in a conductor by creating a change in the magnetic field.

5. _____

6. The definition of an inductor is:
   a. Any part of a circuit that opposes a change in current.
   b. Any part of a circuit that opposes a change in resistance.
   c. A component which produces electricity by electromagnetic induction.
   d. A component which produces resistance using electromagnetic induction.

6. _____

7. Diagram the two symbols which represent a basic inductor.

8. The unit of measurement for an inductor is:
   a. Farad.
   b. Ohm.
   c. Watt.
   d. Henry.

8. _____

9. List the four items which affect the amount of inductance in a coil.

_____

_____

_____

_____

10. The formula to add inductor values in series is the same as that for _____.

10. _____

11. The formula to add inductor values in parallel is the same as that for _____.

11. _____

12. How much current will flow in the series circuit diagrammed below?

12. _____

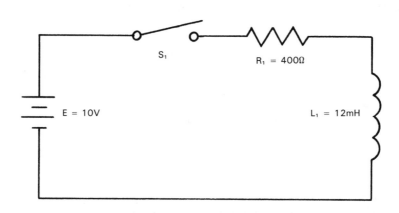

S_1

$R_1 = 400\Omega$

$E = 10V$

$L_1 = 12mH$

13. When two coils of wire are close enough to be linked by a magnetic field, they are said to have:
    a. Mutual inductance.
    b. Been spliced together.
    c. Mutual resistance.
    d. Formed a dc circuit.

13. _____

14. The purpose of a transformer is to:
    a. Step up and down resistance.
    b. Step up and down capacitance.
    c. Step up and down inductance.
    d. Step up and down voltage.

14. _____

15. The function of a transformer is based on the principle of: 15. _____
    a. Core action.
    b. Coefficient of coupling.
    c. Mutual inductance.
    d. Core lamination.

16. Eddy current losses in a transformer are reduced by: 16. _____
    a. Using U-shaped laminations for its core.
    b. Coating the laminations with varnish or an oxide layer.
    c. Keeping the primary separated from the secondary.
    d. Winding the primary in the opposite direction as the secondary.

17. Label the two types of transformers shown below.   A. _____

                                                                                   B. _____

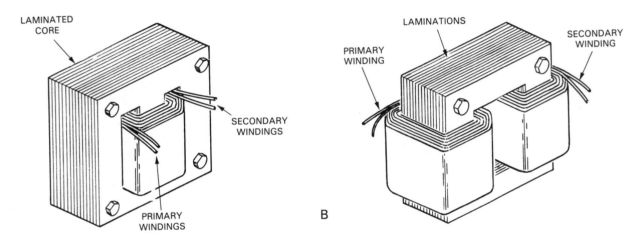

18. Calculate the voltage of the secondary windings in the   18. _____
transformer shown below. Show your work.

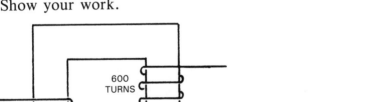

19. In the perfect transformer, secondary power will: 19. _____
    a. Be half that of the primary power.
    b. Be equal to the primary power.
    c. Will be twice that of the primary power.
    d. Will be 1/4 that of the primary power.

 **12** Motors

Name _____   Score _____

Date_____ Class/period_____   Instructor _____

OVERALL OBJECTIVE: You will be able to explain the operation of a motor and identify critical motor components.

DIRECTIONS: Carefully read Chapter 12 of the text. Then complete the following questions, problems, and activities.

1. Label the parts of this simple dc motor.

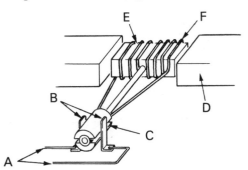

A. _____
B. _____
C. _____
D. _____
E. _____
F. _____

2. Live five appliances where electric motors are used.

_____

_____

_____

_____

_____

3. Examine the name plates on three motors. They will contain information, such as the manufacturer, horsepower, and rpm. Record the manufacturer and horsepower in the chart below. Then, based on the horsepower and the cost of electricity in your area, calculate how much it would cost to run the motor for one hour. (The calculation for horsepower into watts is found in the Dictionary of Terms in the back of the text.)

Cost of electricity (kWh) = _____

MOTOR	MANUFACTURER	HORSEPOWER	COST PER HOUR
1.			
2.			
3.			

4. Draw the electrical symbols for a motor and generator.

MOTOR	GENERATOR

5. The function of a motor is to:
   a. Convert voltage into current.
   b. Convert mechanical energy into electrical energy.
   c. Convert electrical energy into potential energy.
   d. Convert electrical energy into mechanical energy.

5. _____

6. A squirrel cage induction motor received that name because:
   a. Its brushes are the shape of a squirrel's tail.
   b. Of the design of the bearings which support the shaft.
   c. The armature design looks like a squirrel cage.
   d. The coils are made from the same type steel used to make cages.

6. _____

7. True or false? You can use an ac motor with a dc power source.

7. _____

8. DC motor brushes are usually made of:
   a. Copper plates.
   b. Carbon material.
   c. Fine steel wire.
   d. Nylon strings.

8. _____

9. On an induction motor, the difference between the rotating speed of the rotor and that of the magnetic field is called _____.

9. _____

10. The speed of a synchronous motor is determined by:
    a. AC frequency and number of poles.
    b. AC frequency and voltage.
    c. Current and resistance of the circuit.
    d. Inductance of the brushes and number of poles.

10. _____

11. How many poles are needed to make a synchronous motor run at 900 rpm? Show the formula and your work.

11. _____

12. True or false? The output from a dc generator is not pure dc.

12. _____

13. Label the parts of the simple ac generator below.

A. _____
B. _____
C. _____
D. _____

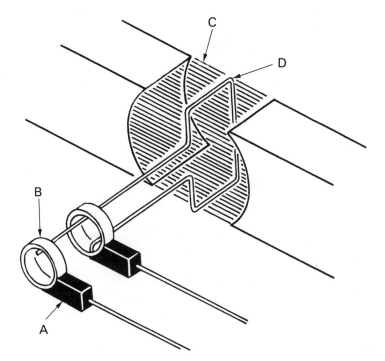

13 Reactance and Impedance

Name _____   Score _____

Date_____ Class/period_____   Instructor _____

OVERALL OBJECTIVE: You will be able to calculate the reactance and impedance of typical circuits.

DIRECTIONS: Carefully read Chapter 13 of the text. Then complete the following questions, problems, and activities.

1. Connect the circuit shown in the diagram below.

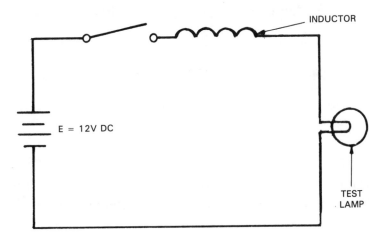

Obtain a stopwatch or a watch with a second hand. Close the switch and record how long it takes for the lamp to reach full brilliance.

Connect the same circuit, but use a 12 volt ac power source instead. Close the switch and record how long it takes for the lamp to light.

Now answer the following questions.

A. How long did it take for the lamp to reach full brilliance in the dc circuit?

A. _____

B. How long did it take the lamp to reach its final brightness in the ac circuit?

B. _____

C. Did the lamp in the ac circuit glow as bright as it did in the dc circuit?

C. _____

Why or why not? _____

_____

_____

2. The opposition offered by inductors to any change in current is called _____ _____.

2. _____

3. What is the characteristic of an ac circuit which causes an inductor to resist current more than it does in a dc circuit?

_____

_____

_____

4. The unit of measurement for inductive reactance is _____.

4. _____

5. In a purely inductive circuit, the:
   a. Voltage lags the current.
   b. Current lags the voltage.
   c. Current and voltage are in phase.
   d. The sum of voltage and current is always equal to one.

5. _____

6. In an RL circuit, the R stands for ____(A)____ and the L stands for ____(B)____.

A. _____

B. _____

7. In an RL circuit, you calculate total voltage drop using:
   a. Addition.
   b. Integration.
   c. Division.
   d. Vectors.

7. _____

8. The circuit diagrammed below has an inductor and resistor. Given the voltage drop across the inductor and resistor in the chart below, calculate the voltage of the power source.

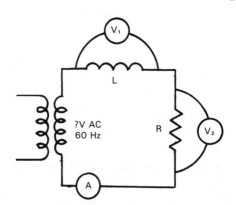

CIRCUIT	VOLTAGE DROPS		POWER SOURCE VOLTAGE
	V_1	V_2	
A.	6.0	6.8	
B.	44.8	40.0	
C.	88.3	65.7	
D.	90.0	79.4	
E.	20.8	12.0	

9. The definition of impedance is:

    9. _____

  a. The opposition offered by inductors to any change in current.

  b. The opposition offered by capacitors to a change in voltage.

  c. The total opposition that an electrical circuit offers to flow of varying current at a given frequency.

  d. A solid state device used for switching and/or amplifying the flow of electrons in a circuit.

10. Look at the two transformers below and note the placement of the terminals. Answer whether the primary and secondary windings are in phase or out of phase.

    A. _____

    B. _____

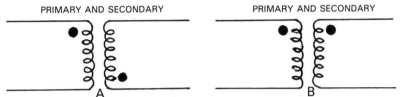

11. A device that stores electrons until they are needed by the circuit is called a _____.

    11. _____

12. Obtain two capacitors and two resistors. Mark the capacitors C_1 and C_2. Mark the resistors R_1 and R_2. Record resistor and capacitor values below.

  R_1 value = _____ohms C_1 value = _____farads

  R_2 value = _____ohms C_2 value = _____farads

Hook up the circuit as shown in the following diagram.

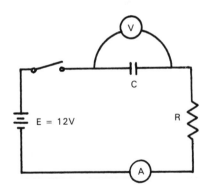

For each resistor and capacitor combination, you are going to close the switch and time how long it takes for the voltmeter to read full voltage. Remember to safely discharge the capacitors after charging them. Record your findings in the chart below.

CIRCUIT	RESISTOR	CAPACITOR	TIME TO REACH FULL VOLTAGE
A.	R_1	C_1	
B.	R_1	C_2	
C.	R_2	C_1	
D.	R_2	C_2	

13. Based on the results of Exercise 12, answer the following questions.
    A. With the same resistor, what time effect did using a larger capacitor have?

    _____

    _____

    B. With the same capacitor, what time effect did using a larger ohm resistor have?

    _____

    _____

14. Hook up a 12 volt bulb, switch, non-polarized capacitor of about 50 μF, and a variable 12 volt ac power supply in series. (See the diagram below.) Close the switch and observe the lamp. Repeat the process without the capacitor.

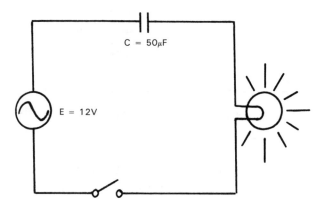

C = 50μF

E = 12V

Was there any difference in the brightness of the lamp with and without the capacitor? _____. If yes, explain why. _____

    _____

    _____

15. In the boxes below, give the formula to find the value indicated under the box.

CAPACITIVE REACTANCE   IMPEDANCE IN AN RC CIRCUIT   CURRENT IN AN RC CIRCUIT

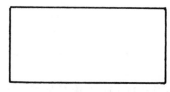

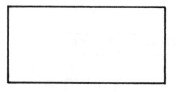 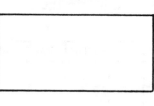

VOLTAGE DROP OVER A CAPACITOR IN AN RC CIRCUIT   VOLTAGE DROP OVER RESISTOR IN AN RC CIRCUIT   TOTAL VOLTAGE USING VECTOR ADDITION

16. The diagram below shows an RC circuit with a 60 Hz ac power supply. The chart below the diagram gives values for the power supply voltage, resistor, and capacitor for five different circuits. Using the proper formulas, find capacitive reactance, impedance, current, and voltage drop across the capacitor and resistor. Find these values for each of the five circuits given in the chart. Calculate your answers to two decimal places (0.00).

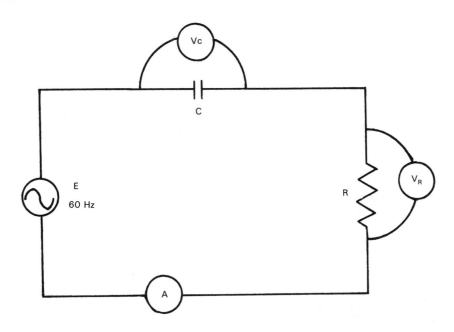

CIRCUIT	POWER SUPPLY VOLTAGE E	RESISTOR (OHMS) R	CAPACITOR (MICRO-FARADS) C	CAPACITIVE RESISTANCE (OHMS) X_c	IMPEDANCE (OHMS) Z	CURRENT (AMPERES) I	VOLTAGE DROPS	
							CAPACITOR V_C	RESISTOR V_R
A.	30	9	221					
B.	100	5	221					
C.	120	12	156					
D.	250	15	133					
E.	240	18	110					

14 LCR Circuits

Name _____   Score _____

Date_____ Class/period_____   Instructor _____

OVERALL OBJECTIVE: You will be able to calculate the impedance of an LCR circuit and design a resonant circuit.

DIRECTIONS: Carefully read Chapter 14 of the text. Then complete the following questions, problems, and activities.

1. What three items does an LCR circuit contain?   1. _____
   a. Load, control, and reactance.
   b. Load, capacitance, and reactance.
   c. Inductance, capacitance, and reactance.
   d. Inductance, capacitance, and resistance.

2. Label the components of the LCR circuit shown below.

   A. _____
   B. _____
   C. _____
   D. _____

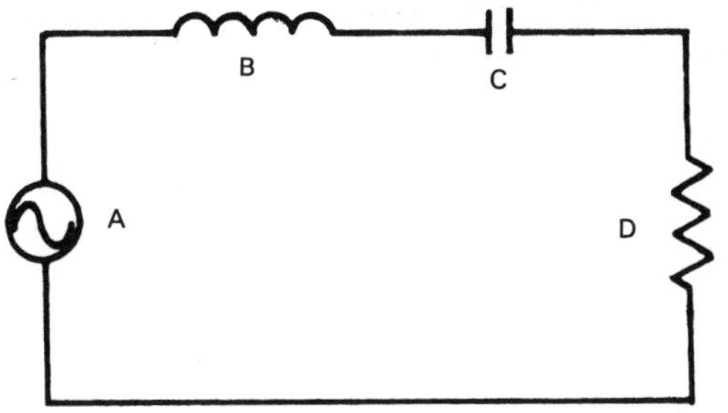

3. When solving for inductive reactance in an ac circuit, you   3. _____
   are finding:
   a. Equivalent amount of resistance caused by having an
      inductor in the circuit.
   b. Amount of voltage drop caused by having a capacitor
      in the circuit.
   c. Reduction in current flow caused by the inductor.
   d. Number of microhenrys present in the circuit.

4. Why are inductive reactance and capacitive reactance opposing actions? _____
_____
_____
_____
_____

5. The diagram below shows an LCR circuit with a 100 Hz ac power supply. The chart below the diagram gives values for the power supply voltage, resistor, capacitor, and inductor. Using the formulas and examples given in Chapter 14, solve for capacitive reactance, inductive reactance, net reactance, impedance, current, and voltage drop across the inductor, capacitor, and resistor. Calculate these values for each of the five circuits given in the chart. Calculate your answers to two decimal places.

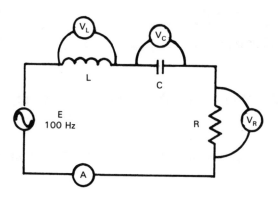

		CIRCUIT A	CIRCUIT B	CIRCUIT C	CIRCUIT D	CIRCUIT E
Power Supply Voltage (volts) E		110	12	150	90	240
Resistor (ohms) R		10	15	20	40	100
Inductor (henrys) L		0.300	0.236	0.219	0.324	7.400
Capacitor (microfarads) C		18.2	11.4	10.6	13.7	500.00
Capacitive Reactance (ohms) X_C						
Inductive Reactance (ohms) X_L						
Net Reactance (ohms) $X_L - X_C$						
Impedance (ohms) Z						
Current (amps) A						
Voltage Drop	V_R					
	V_L					
	V_C					

6. For each of the circuits in Exercise 5, change the capacitor value to make the circuit resonant. Remember $X_L = X_C$ when the circuit is resonant.

CIRCUIT	CAPACITOR (MICROFARADS)	CHANGE CAPACITOR VALUE TO:
A	18.2	
B	11.4	
C	10.6	
D	13.7	
E	500.00	

 **15** Filters

Name _____   Score _____

Date_____ Class/period_____   Instructor _____

OVERALL OBJECTIVE: You will be able to identify the purpose of a filter and design circuits to filter out unwanted frequencies.

DIRECTIONS: Carefully read Chapter 15 of the text. Then complete the following questions, problems, and activities.

1. One of the functions of an LCR circuit is to:
   a. Lower the voltage of the power supply.
   b. Filter out unwanted frequencies.
   c. Act as a barrier for all ac and dc circuits.
   d. Eliminate the hum found in radio frequencies below 20 Hz.

1. _____

2. When a circuit reaches resonant frequency:
   a. The impedance of the circuit is at a minimum.
   b. The impedance of the circuit is at its highest value.
   c. The voltage across all portions of the circuit are at their lowest level.
   d. Additional capacitance must be added to prevent overloading the circuit.

2. _____

3. To make a circuit resonate at a desired frequency, you should:
   a. Increase the size of the capacitor.
   b. Reduce the size of the inductor.
   c. Carefully choose the right power supply voltage.
   d. Choose the proper inductor and capacitor.

3. _____

MATCHING: Match the filter name to its proper definition. Print the letter of the appropriate filter next to the number.

4. Filters out frequencies above and below the resonant frequency.

    a. Low pass filter.
    b. Capacitor.
    c. Band pass filter.
    d. Inductor.
    e. Bandstop filter.
    f. High pass filter.

4. _____

5. Filters out frequencies close to the resonant frequency.

5. _____

6. Filters out all low frequencies.

6. _____

7. Filters out all high frequencies.

7. _____

8. Reduces ac ripple of the power supply output.

8. _____

9. The Q of a circuit is defined as the:
    a. Ratio of the reactance of an inductor or capacitor to circuit resistance.
    b. Peak value of the ac sine wave.
    c. Filtering effect created by adding capacitance.
    d. Unwanted frequencies in a reduced voltage circuit.

9. _____

10. The diagram below shows an LCR circuit with a resonant frequency of 60 Hz and an inductive reactance of 400 ohms. Calculate what range of frequencies is passed by this filter. Show your work and any formulas required.

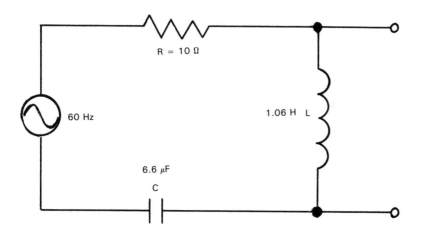

With the circuit at resonant frequency, the filter will pass a band of frequencies from _____(A)_____ to _____(B)_____.

A. _____

B. _____

11. The diagram below shows a simple series LCR circuit with a 1 mV power supply, 134 μH inductor, 10 ohm resistor, and 201 pF capacitor. Determine the resonant frequency of the circuit and record it in the middle row of the chart below. Also record the inductive reactance, capacitive reactance, impedance, and voltage drops at the resonant frequency. Then mark frequencies 200, 400, and 600 kHz above and below the resonant frequency. Record the inductive reactance, capacitive reactance, impedance, and voltage drops for each of those frequencies. Round your answers to the nearest whole number.

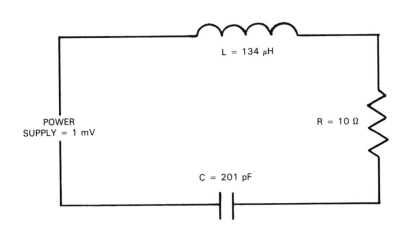

L = 134 μH

POWER SUPPLY = 1 mV

R = 10 Ω

C = 201 pF

	FREQUENCY kHz	VOLTAGE E	INDUCTIVE REACTANCE (OHMS) X_L	CAPACITIVE REACTANCE (OHMS) X_C	RESISTANCE (OHMS) R	IMPEDANCE (OHMS) Z	VOLTAGE DROPS (μV) V_L	VOLTAGE DROPS (μV) V_C
−600 kHz		1mV			10			
−400 kHz		1mV			10			
−200 kHz		1 mV			10			
Resonant Frequency		1 mV			10			
+200 kHz		1 mV			10			
+400 kHz		1 mV			10			
+600 kHz		1 mV			10			

12. Looking at the chart in Exercise 11, what do you notice about the voltage drops across the inductor and capacitor at the resonant frequency compared to those at other frequencies?

_____

_____

_____

13. Refer to the chart in Exercise 11. How does the impedance for the circuit at resonant frequency differ from the impedance above and below the resonant frequency?

_____

_____

_____

16 Diodes

Name _____   Score _____

Date_____ Class/period_____   Instructor _____

OVERALL OBJECTIVE: You will be able to identify the function of a diode and design circuits in which diodes are used.

DIRECTIONS: Carefully read Chapter 16 of the text. Then complete the following questions, problems, and activities.

1. Which of the following are solid state devices?
   a. Resistor, capacitor, and inductor.
   b. Diode, transistor, and SCR.
   c. Conductor, insulator, and semiconductor.
   d. Fuse, thermistor, and diode.

3. _____

2. A diode is designed to:
   a. Permit electron flow in only one direction.
   b. Restrict electron flow in two directions.
   c. Increase the capacitance of a PN junction.
   d. Produce overloads in high current circuits.

2. _____

3. Mark arrows on the two diagrams shown below to indicate current flow. If no current flows, mark "no current."

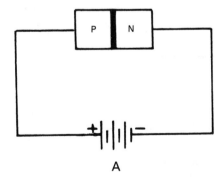

A

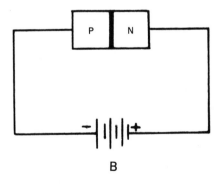

B

4. Look at the diagrams in Exercise 3. For both A and B, indicate whether the diode is forward-biased or reverse-biased. Place your answers at the right.

A. _____
B. _____

5. The amount of voltage which a reverse-biased diode can take without being damaged is called _____ _____ _____.

6. Look at the diagrams shown below. What is the maximum amount of current the diodes will pass without either of the diodes being damaged?

A. _____

B. _____

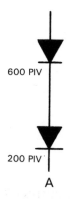

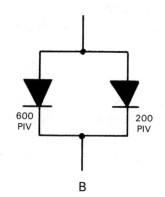

7. For the two diagrams shown below, what is the maximum peak inverse voltage the diodes will handle before one of the diodes is damaged?

A. _____

B. _____

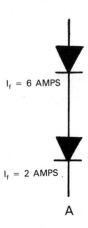

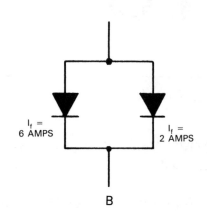

8. Label the anode and cathode of the diode symbol below.

A. _____

B. _____

A ────────▶|──────── B

9. When placing a diode in a circuit:
   a. The anode should be connected to the negative terminal.
   b. The anode should be connected to the positive terminal.
   c. The cathodes should be connected to the positive terminal.
   d. It does not matter which direction you place the diode.

9. _____

10. Before checking a diode for polarity with an ohmmeter, you should:
    a. Ground the negative side of the diode.
    b. Be sure that the circuit power to the diode is on.
    c. Check that the battery installed matches ohmmeter + and − marks.
    d. Touch the ohmmeter leads together and set the meter for infinite readings.

10. _____

11. What colors would be painted on the side of the diode which is labeled 1N131?

A. _____

B. _____

C. _____

12. Another name for a diode which is constructed to allow current flow in both directions is a:
    a. Germanium diode.
    b. Silicon diode.
    c. Zener diode.
    d. Rectifier diode.

12. _____

13. Obtain three diodes, one of which should be a power diode. Measure the resistance using a vacuum tube voltmeter or other suitable ohmmeter having at least six resistance levels. Measure the diode's resistance biased both in the forward and reverse direction. Record your answers in the chart below. (Refer to Fig. 16-20, page 220, of the text for an example.)

RESISTANCE VALUES

	POWER DIODE 1 Code #_____		DIODE 2 Code #_____		DIODE 3 Code #_____	
	Forward	Reverse	Forward	Reverse	Forward	Reverse
R X 1						
R X 10						
R X 100						
R X 1000						
R X 10K						
R X 100K						
R X 1 MEG						

14. Connect a dc series circuit as shown in schematic A below. In the chart below, record the current and the voltage drops across the lamps. Next, place a diode in the circuit as shown in schematic B. Record the current and voltage drops across the lamps and diode. Then, reverse the direction of the diode and record the values again in the chart below.

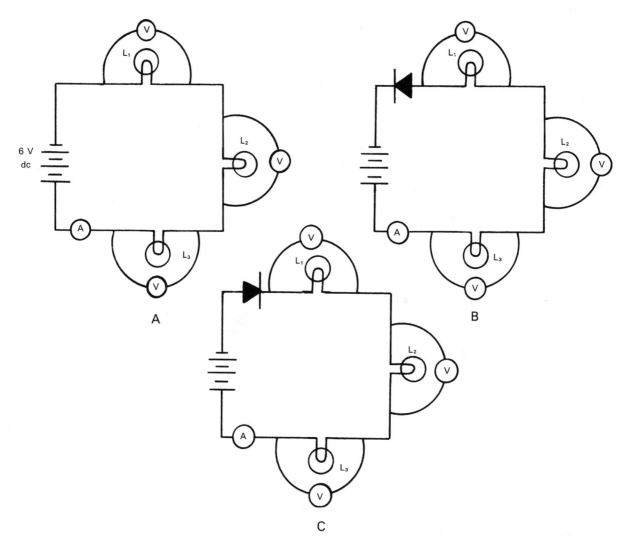

CIRCUIT	CURRENT	VOLTAGE DROPS			
		L₁	L₂	L₃	DIODE
A					
B					
C					

Answer the following questions about the experiment you just completed.
A. How bright were the lamps without the diode (Circuit A)? _____

_____

_____

Diodes

B. With the diode added to the circuit (Circuit B), was there any change in the brilliance of the lamps from Circuit A? _____. If so, why? _____

_____

_____

C. With the diode reversed (Circuit C), was there any change in the brilliance of the lamps? _____. If so why? _____

_____

D. Was there any significant change in voltage drop of the lamps between Circuit A and Circuit B?

_____

_____

_____

E. Was there any significant change in voltage drop of the lamps between Circuit B and Circuit C? _____. If so, why?_____

_____

_____

F. In Circuit B, calculate the resistance of the lamps and diode using your measurements and Ohm's Law. Record your answers in the chart below.

COMPONENT	RESISTANCE
Lamp 1	
Lamp 2	
Lamp 3	
Diode	

15. Connect Circuit B of Exercise 13, only substitute a 6 V ac power source. In the chart below, record the current and voltage drops across the lamps and diode.

CURRENT	VOLTAGE DROPS			
	L_1	L_2	L_3	DIODE

Calculate the resistance of the lamps and diode using your measurements above and Ohm's Law. Record your answers below.

COMPONENT	RESISTANCE
Lamp 1	
Lamp 2	
Lamp 3	
Diode	

16. Explain any differences in the lamp's brightness and voltage drop using a diode in a dc circuit versus an ac circuit.

_____

_____

_____

_____

_____

17. What is the purpose of a full wave rectifier?　　　　17. _____
    a. Convert dc into ac.
    b. Increase or decrease voltage in an ac circuit.
    c. Increase or decrease voltage in a dc circuit.
    d. Convert ac into dc.

18. What is the purpose of zener diode?　　　　18. _____
    a. Increase voltage.
    b. Decrease voltage.
    c. Regulate voltage.
    d. Convert ac into dc.

17 Transistors

Name _____   Score _____

Date_____ Class/period_____   Instructor _____

OVERALL OBJECTIVE: You will be able to identify the purpose and properties of switching and amplifying transistors.

DIRECTIONS: Carefully read Chapter 17 of the text. Then complete the following questions, problems, and activities.

1. A transistor is used in an electronic circuit to:
   a. Allow current flow in both directions.
   b. Protect against the flow of electrons.
   c. Switch and amplify electrical signals.
   d. Permit a current flow of 5 to 10 amperes.

   1. _____

2. A switching circuit is used to:
   a. Turn the flow of electrons on and off.
   b. Slowly build up a high flow of current.
   c. Adjust the capacitance of an inductor.
   d. Combine a photosensor in a circuit.

   2. _____

3. An amplifying circuit is similar to:
   a. A three-way light switch.
   b. A dimmer switch.
   c. Using perforated tape on a numerical control milling machine.
   d. A diode turning on and off.

   3. _____

4. List two common types of transistors.

   4. _____
   _____

5. To permit the flow of electrons in a transistor:
   a. A positive signal must be applied to the base of a PNP transistor.
   b. A negative signal must be applied to the base of a NPN transistor.
   c. No signal is applied to the base of a PNP transistor.
   d. A negative signal must be applied to the base of a PNP transistor.

   5. _____

6. Label the parts of this PNP transistor symbol.

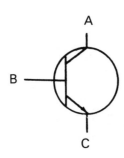

A. _____

B. _____

C. _____

7. True or false? The middle letter of the transistor type provides a clue as to what signal polarity is required to turn the transistor on.

7. _____

8. The lead nearest the tab on a transistor is usually:
   a. The emitter.
   b. The collector.
   c. The base.
   d. Not the same on every transistor.

8. _____

9. Looking at the current flow in the transistors shown below, label them as either PNP or NPN.

A. _____

B. _____

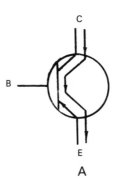

A

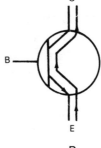

B

10. Label the parts used when installing a power transistor.

A. _____

B. _____

C. _____

D. _____

E. _____

F. _____

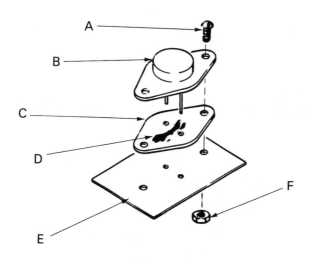

11. Ohmmeter tests are used to determine whether a transistor is the NPN or PNP type. Look at the ohmmeter readings below. For both A and B transistors, determine whether they are NPN or PNP.

A. _____

B. _____

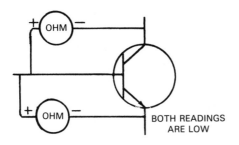

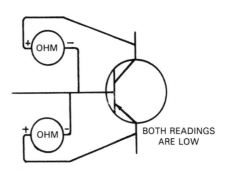

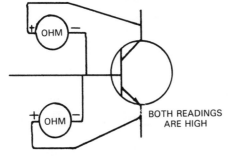

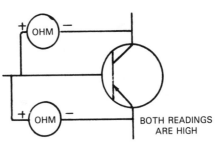

A   B

12. The gain of a transistor refers to the:
    a. Ratio of the beta divided by the gamma.
    b. Voltage required on the base to trigger the transistor on.
    c. Ratio of collector current to base current.
    d. Ratio of the emitter current to base current.

12. _____

13. The beta of most amplifying transistors is:
    a. Usually in the range between 0.1 and 0.99.
    b. Always less than 20.
    c. Usually between 30 and 200.
    d. Most often higher than 500.

13. _____

14. Draw arrows on the diagrams below to show both the base current and main current flow in the two circuits.

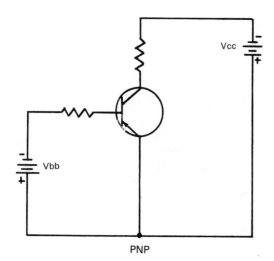

PNP

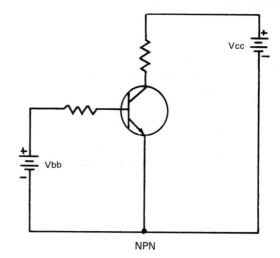

NPN

18 Relays and Switches

Name _____   Score _____

Date_____ Class/period_____   Instructor _____

OVERALL OBJECTIVE: You will be able to identify the purposes and properties of relays and relay circuits.

DIRECTIONS: Carefully read Chapter 18 of the text. Then complete the following questions, problems, and activities.

1. A relay is a device used to:
   a. Increase the current and voltage levels of a solid state circuit.
   b. Decrease the resistance of a circuit to improve its speed of operation.
   c. Act as a switch in electrical circuits.
   d. Match the impedance of a circuit.

1. _____

2. In the boxes below, sketch the types of contacts found on a typical relay.

A. NORMALLY OPEN	B. NORMALLY CLOSED
C. NORMALLY OPEN, TIMED CLOSED	D. NORMALLY CLOSED, TIMED OPEN

3. The coil of a relay can be activated only by:
   a. DC current.
   b. AC current.
   c. Lack of dc current.
   d. AC or dc current.

3. _____

Obtain a relay, switch, wire, buzzer, pushbutton, and a voltmeter from your instructor. Perform the tasks given in Exercises 4, 5, 6, and 7 using these parts.

4. Connect the coil of the relay to a pushbutton and power supply. Set up the circuit so the relay's holding contacts keep the relay energized. Make a sketch below which shows how the circuit is wired.

5. Test whether each set of contacts on the relay is normally open, normally closed, or timed by wiring a buzzer to each of them. Write your findings in the chart below.

CONTACT NUMBER	CONTACT TYPE (Normally Open, Normally Closed, or Timed)
1	
2	
3	
4	
5	
6	
7	
8	

6. Use a voltmeter to take voltage readings in the circuit. Write your findings in the chart below.

LOCATION OF VOLTAGE READING	STATUS OF START BUTTON	MEASURED READING
Across the power supply	not pressed	
Across the relay coil	not pressed	
Across the open contacts	not pressed	
Across the power supply	pressed	
Across the relay coil	pressed	
Across the closed contacts	pressed	

7. Describe one use for each of the following contacts found on timed relays.
   a. Normally open, timed open. _____

   _____

   b. Normally closed, timed open. _____

   _____

   c. Normally open, timed closed. _____

   _____

   d. Normally closed, timed closed. _____

   _____

8. Construct a circuit which can be used to stop a conveyor belt when too many parts or products reach the end of the belt. Use at least one of each of the following items: relay, limit switch, normally open contacts, warning buzzer, and start/stop switch.

9. Provide two uses (other than those described in the chapter) for each of the following items.
   a. Solenoid. _____

   _____

   b. Relay. _____

   _____

   c. Limit switch. _____

   _____

19 Integrated Circuits and Other Solid State Devices

Name _____   Score _____

Date_____ Class/period_____   Instructor _____

OVERALL OBJECTIVE: You will be able to recognize the function of field effect transistors, silicon controlled rectifiers, and integrated circuits.

DIRECTIONS: Carefully read Chapter 19 of the text. Then complete the following questions, problems, and activities.

1. Label the leads of this junction field effect transistor (JFET).

   A. _____

   B. _____

   C. _____

   D. _____

2. An FET is made of:
   a. Three layers; P, N, and P material.
   b. A solid piece of N material with a P gate.
   c. N material only.
   d. P material only.

   2. _____

3. To allow a JFET—N channel FET to pass current, you must:
   a. Increase negative voltage to the gates.
   b. Decrease negative voltage to the gates.
   c. Increase positive voltage to the gates.
   d. Apply no voltage to the gates.

   3. _____

4. Which of the following components are shipped with their leads shorted to prevent damage from static electricity?
   a. SCR.
   b. MOSFET.
   c. JFET.
   d. Diode.

   4. _____

5. Label the parts of this metal oxide semiconductor field effect transistor (MOSFET).

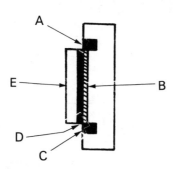

A.

B. _____

C. _____

D. _____

E. _____

6. Which of the following components is used for controlling high current circuits (20 amps or more)?
   a. SCR.
   b. JFET.
   c. IC.
   d. MOSFET.

6. _____

7. One method used to turn off an SCR is to:
   a. Make the gate positive.
   b. Make the gate negative.
   c. Remove any signal on the gate.
   d. Open a switch wired in series with the SCR.

7. _____

8. In an ac circuit, an SCR can be turned on any time during:
   a. The positive alternation.
   b. The negative alternation.
   c. A time of zero current.
   d. A time of zero voltage.

8. _____

9. Give the component name for the symbols shown below.

A.

B. _____

C. _____

D. _____

E. _____

F. _____

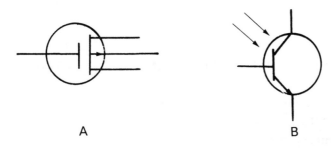

A

B

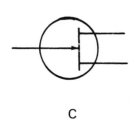

C

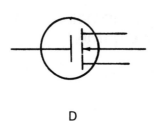

D

E

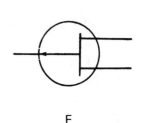

F

10. An integrated circuit is a very small circuit containing hundreds of _____, _____, _____, and _____.

10. _____

_____

_____

_____

11. An AND gate with three input leads will have output when:
    a. Signals are present at inputs 1 and 2.
    b. Signals are present at inputs 2 and 3.
    c. No signals are present on any of its input leads.
    d. Signals are present at all three inputs.

11. _____

12. When you undercut a PC board during manufacture:
    a. The circuit is weakened.
    b. The circuit is strengthened.
    c. Extra solder should be added to the board.
    d. The board is a high quality component.

12. _____

13. List seven places in your home where you can find integrated circuits.

_____

_____

_____

_____

_____

_____

_____

14. List seven places in your community where you can find integrated circuits.

_____

_____

_____

_____

_____

_____

_____

 **20** Computers

Name _____   Score _____

Date_____ Class/period_____   Instructor _____

OVERALL OBJECTIVE: You will be able to describe the many parts of a computer and explain their function.

DIRECTIONS: Carefully read Chapter 20 of the text. Then complete the following question, problems, and activities.

1. With the power disconnected, work with your instructor in taking a computer apart. Identify the parts inside. Trace the electrical path through the various parts of the computer. Begin with the power supply and trace a path to the output on the computer's monitor.

2. List at least seven important components found inside a PC.

_____

_____

_____

_____

_____

_____

_____

_____

3. Complete the chart below. List at least five businesses in your area. Show the different computer uses you might find in each of the businesses you list.

Business/Company Name	Occupations	Computer Uses

4. Make a list of at least five places where you see applications for computers.

   Computers used in - Application

   Examples:

        Sewing machines - Controls the type of stitching.
        Carpet industry - Create the designs on carpets.

   _____

   _____

   _____

   _____

   _____

5. List four microprocessors and list the speed(s) at which they run.

   _____

   _____

   _____

   _____

6. Make a list of computer programs and their costs. Find the most expensive and least expensive programs. What are the reasons for the big differences in the cost of the two programs?

   _____

   _____

   _____

   _____

   _____

   _____

   _____

   _____

   _____

7. Use a computer to prepare of spreadsheet for a simple budget.

8. Select one of your favorite computer games. How much memory is required to load that program on the computer? What percent of the total memory on your hard drive? How is the memory used labeled? _____

   _____

9. A list of businesses and industries follows. Give at least three different ways that computers could be used by each of them.

   A. Clothing store

       1. _____

       2. _____

       3. _____

B. Road building companies

1. _____

2. _____

3. _____

C. Stock markets

1. _____

2. _____

3. _____

D. Lawyers

1. _____

2. _____

3. _____

E. Drug stores/pharmacists

1. _____

2. _____

3. _____

F. Insurance agents/brokers

1. _____

2. _____

3. _____

10. Using the list of computer applications shown below, identify a company, business or industry near you where they might be used.

A. Inventory of raw materials

_____

_____

B. List of books being sold and their cost

_____

_____

C. Blueprints or floor plans of houses being built in a community

_____

_____

D. Amount of tax due on a piece of property

_____

_____

E. Cost of plumbing materials, sinks and bathroom cabinets

_____

_____

F. List of styles and cost for eyeglasses being sold

_____

_____

11. The binary code number 1001101 is equal to what base 10 number?_____

    A. 155

    B. 77

    C. 45

    D. 4

Fill in the blanks:

12. The temporary memory of a computer is called _____ while the permanent memory is called _____. When the computer is shut off, all the information stored in _____ is lost unless it has been saved on _____.

 **21** Fiber Optics

Name _____   Score _____

Date_____ Class/period_____   Instructor _____

OVERALL OBJECTIVE: You will be able to identify the purposes and properties of fiber optics and how it relates to the field of electricity and electronics.

DIRECTIONS: Carefully read Chapter 21 of the text. Then complete the following questions, problems, and activities.

1. Fiber optics technology consists of: 1. _____
   a. Hollow copper tubes used to carry electrons.
   b. Solid plastic rods used to carry electrons.
   c. A hollow solid state component made of several ICs.
   d. Solid glass strands which carry photons.

2. The pulses used with fiber optics are: 2. _____
   a. Electrons emitted by a high speed transformer.
   b. Light signals which are emitted by either an LED or a laser diode.
   c. Triggered by high speed relay circuits.
   d. Brought into the circuitry by the SCR turning on and off.

3. Explain why fewer repeater stations are required with fiber optics installations.

   _____
   _____
   _____
   _____
   _____

4. List four advantages fiber optics have over conventional methods of signal transmission.

   _____
   _____
   _____
   _____

5. List two problems found with fiber optics compared to conventional methods of signal transmission.

_____

_____

6. Obtain a piece of fiber optics cable and a light source. Test the fiber's ability to transmit light through curves. Direct the light source straight at the fibers. Record your findings in the chart below.

ANGLE	ABILITY TO TRANSMIT LIGHT			
	Excellent	Fair	Poor	No Light Passage
30 degrees				
45 degrees				
90 degrees				
120 degrees				

7. True or False? The angle you bend the fiber optics cable affects the light transmitted.

7. _____

8. Change the angle of the light source being directed at the fiber to those angles shown in the chart below. Keep the fiber itself straight. Record your findings.

ANGLE	ABILITY TO TRANSMIT LIGHT			
	Excellent	Fair	Poor	No Light Passage
30 degrees				
45 degrees				
90 degrees				

9. Does the angle of the light source make any difference in a fiber's light transmission?_____ If so, why?_____

_____

_____

_____

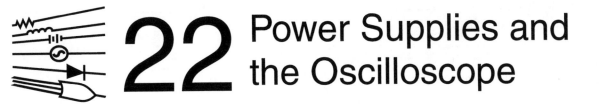

22 Power Supplies and the Oscilloscope

Name _____   Score _____

Date _____ Class/period _____   Instructor _____

OVERALL OBJECTIVE: You will be able to identify common power supplies and adapt new ones for your needs. You will also be able to recognize the function of an oscilloscope for analyzing circuits.

DIRECTIONS: Carefully read Chapter 22 of the text. Then complete the following questions, problems, and activities.

1. List three advantages of using batteries as a power source.

    _____

    _____

    _____

2. A converter is used to change:
    a. AC to dc.
    b. DC to ac.
    c. AC from one voltage to a different ac voltage.
    d. DC from one voltage to a different dc voltage.

    2. _____

3. A line regulator is used to:
    a. Change ac to dc.
    b. Change dc to ac.
    c. Change ac from one voltage to a different ac voltage.
    d. Change dc from one voltage to a different dc voltage.

    3. _____

4. The main disadvantage of a regulated power supply compared to an unregulated supply is:
    a. Higher cost.
    b. Less voltage regulation.
    c. Less control.
    d. Lower current regulation.

    4. _____

5. A diode connected to the secondary of a transformer will produce:
    a. AC.
    b. Pulsating dc.
    c. Fully rectified dc.
    d. DC with no ripple.

    5. _____

6. Ripple in dc circuits can be reduced using:
   a. Capacitors in the circuit.
   b. Resistors in the circuit.
   c. Inductors in the circuit.
   d. One diode on the transformer secondary.

6. _____

7. Placing diodes on each of the outside leads of a 12 volt center tap transformer secondary will:
   a. Increase the output to 24 volts.
   b. Reduce the output voltage to 3 volts dc.
   c. Change the output voltage to 6 volts dc.
   d. Produces either 12 volts dc or 12 volts ac.

7. _____

8. Half wave pulsating dc results from:
   a. A second transformer connected in series with the circuit.
   b. Using a capacitor with less than 5 RC time constants.
   c. A battery nearing the end of its usable life.
   d. A diode in a full wave bridge rectifier having been destroyed.

8. _____

9. Explain what is meant by feedback in an electrical circuit.

   _____
   _____
   _____
   _____
   _____

10. The part of a scope which produces the image is the:
    a. Graticule.
    b. CRT.
    c. TEC.
    d. Axis.

10. _____

11. To read the voltage level of a power source, you would:
    a. Reduce the level of the electron beam.
    b. Observe the X axis of the scope.
    c. Observe the Y axis of the scope.
    d. Widen the trace on the X axis.

11. _____

12. The Lissajous figure which tells you that the two frequencies being measured are equal is:
    a. A line.
    b. A figure eight.
    c. A rolling infinity.
    d. A circle.

12. _____

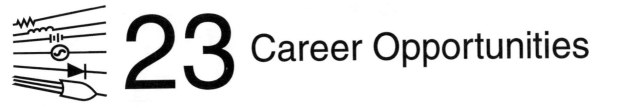

23 Career Opportunities

Name _____   Score _____

Date_____ Class/period_____   Instructor _____

OVERALL OBJECTIVE: You will be able to recognize the many electricity and electronics careers you might choose to pursue.

DIRECTIONS: Carefully read Chapter 23 of the text. Then complete the following activities.

Careers in the electricity/electronics area can be broken down into five basic categories. They are listed below. Information about these and many other jobs in this field can be obtained at your library, from employment agencies, from persons in the field, and in books, such as the Dictionary of Occupational Titles.

List careers in each of the five areas. Find at least three. Do not use those listed in the text. Select one career from each area. Find information about that job and its qualifications, including: schooling, salary, working hours, physical requirements, licenses, and certificates required. When you are finished, circle the job you would like the most.

CONSTRUCTION WORKERS

JOBS IN THIS AREA

1. _____
2. _____
3. _____

QUALIFICATIONS FOR JOB: _____

1. _____
2. _____
3. _____
4. _____
5. _____

MAINTENANCE WORKERS

JOBS IN THIS AREA

1. _____
2. _____
3. _____

QUALIFICATIONS FOR JOB: _____

1. _____
2. _____
3. _____
4. _____
5. _____

TECHNICIANS

JOBS IN THIS AREA

1. _____
2. _____
3. _____

QUALIFICATIONS FOR JOB: _____

1. _____
2. _____
3. _____
4. _____
5. _____

ENGINEERS

JOBS IN THIS AREA

1. _____
2. _____
3. _____

QUALIFICATIONS FOR JOB: _____

1. _____
2. _____
3. _____
4. _____
5. _____

SUPERVISORS

JOBS IN THIS AREA

1. _____
2. _____
3. _____

QUALIFICATIONS FOR JOB: _____

1. _____
2. _____
3. _____
4. _____
5. _____